SNOOPY STARS

— AS —

THE WORLD FAMOUS LITERARY ACE

Charles M. Schulz

ℛℛ

RAVETTE BOOKS

First published by
Ravette Books Limited 1988

Printed and bound in Great Britain
for Ravette Books Limited,
3 Glenside Estate, Star Road, Partridge Green,
Horsham, Sussex RH13 8RA
by Cox & Wyman Ltd, Reading

ISBN 1 85304 066 5

PEANUTS

Helen Sweetstory was born on a small farm on April 5, 1950.

I THINK I'LL SKIP ALL THE STUFF ABOUT HER PARENTS AND GRANDPARENTS...THAT'S ALWAYS KIND OF BORING...

2-25

I'LL ALSO SKIP ALL THE STUFF ABOUT HER STUPID CHILDHOOD... I'LL GO RIGHT TO WHERE THE ACTION BEGAN...

It was raining the night of her high-school prom.

PEANUTS

Helen Sweetstory was born on a small farm on April 5, 1950. It was raining the night of her High-School prom.

"LATER THAT SUMMER SHE WAS THROWN FROM A HORSE..A TALL, DARK STRANGER CARRIED HER BACK TO THE STABLES...WAS THIS THE LOVE SHE HAD BEEN SEEKING? TWO YEARS LATER, IN PARIS, SHE.."

2-29

IN PARIS?! WHAT ABOUT THE TALL, DARK STRANGER? YOU NEVER GO INTO DETAIL!

WHAT KIND OF A BIOGRAPHER ARE YOU?

I'M A GENTLEMAN BIOGRAPHER!

SCHULZ

PEANUTS

Things I've Learned After It Was Too Late

6-28

Never argue with the cat next door. He's always right

PEANUTS Tm Reg. U.S. Pat. Off. - All rights reserved
© 1973 by United Feature Syndicate, Inc.

The Bunnies - A Tale of Mirth and Woe.

"Ha Ha Ha," laughed the bunnies.

"Ha Ha Ha Ha Ha Ha Ha Ha Ha Ha Ha Ha"

SO MUCH FOR THE MIRTH!

4-25

PEANUTS

Though her husband often went on business trips, she hated to be left alone.

"I've solved our problem," he said. "I've bought you a St. Bernard. It's name is Great Reluctance."

"Now, when I go away, you shall know that I am leaving you with Great Reluctance!"

She hit him with a waffle iron.

PEANUTS

His wife had always
hated his work.

9-18

"You'll never make any
money growing toadstools,"
she complained.

"On the contrary," he
declared. "My toadstool
business is mushrooming!"

She creamed him with
the electric toaster.

PEANUTS

Dutch Waltz, the famous skater, was worried.

His skating partner, Chil Blain, was in love.

While playing a show in Denver, she had become involved with a cowboy named Martin Gale.

THE STORY ISN'T MUCH, BUT THE NAMES ARE GREAT!

4-2

SCHULZ

Immediately after he won the golf tournament, he was interviewed on TV.

"This is the most exciting moment of my life!" he said.

"I saw you on TV," said his wife. "I thought the day we got married was the most exciting moment of your life."

In his next tournament, he failed to make the cut.

4-4   SCHULZ

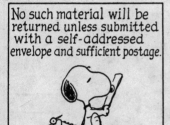

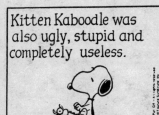

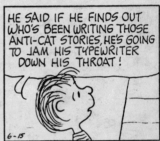

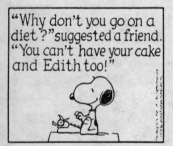

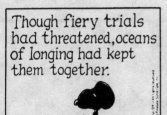

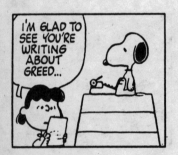

Joe Swimming ran a pool service.

When he and his wife had their first daughter, they couldn't decide on a name.

"How about Chlorine?" suggested Joe.

His wife hit him with a pool sweep.

I KNOW WHAT WE SHOULD DO! WE'RE ALL TOGETHER HERE SO WE SHOULD HAVE OUR PICTURE TAKEN...

WE'LL SEND IT HOME TO MOM AND DAD...

And that's the story of how two soldiers and their sister met in France during World War I.

5-11

And I don't care if anyone believes me or not.

Gentlemen,
Regarding the recent rejection slip you sent me.

11-13

I think there might have been a misunderstanding.

What I really wanted was for you to publish my story, and send me fifty thousand dollars.

Didn't you realize that?

Dear Contributor,

Thank you for considering us with your manuscript.

Has it ever occurred to you that you may be the worst writer in the history of the world?

3-12

I HAVE A UNIQUE COLLECTION OF REJECTION SLIPS...

© 1982 United Feature Syndicate, Inc.

They could never agree on anything.

"Why don't we truck on down to the bike shop?" she asked.

"No," he said. "Let's bike on down to the truck shop."

Their marriage counselor was not at all encouraging.

Spring.

3-27

© 1982 United Feature Syndicate, Inc.

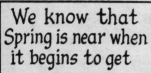

We know that
Spring is near when
it begins to get

windy.

Beauty Tips

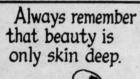

Always remember
that beauty is
only skin deep.

© 1982 United Feature Syndicate, Inc.

5-10

fur deep.

Beauty Tips

Always remember
that beauty is
only fur deep.

5-11

© 1982 United Feature Syndicate, Inc.

feather deep.

Travel Tips

8-30

How to avoid carsickness, seasickness and airsickness...

Be careful what you eat.

And stay home.

Health Tips.

9-3

When you are looking under your dresser for something you've lost, don't bump your head

© 1982 United Feature Syndicate, Inc.

And don't say I didn't warn you.

Schulz

"You love hockey more than you love me!" she complained.

11-23

"You love those hockey gloves, and shinguards, and skates and elbow pads more than you love me!"

"That's not true!" he said.

© 1982 United Feature Syndicate, Inc.

"I love you much more than I love my elbow pads."

He was a huge man
with a fierce and wild
expression, and eyes

like

a teeny tiny
little yellow bird.

11-30

Other Snoopy titles published by Ravette Books

Snoopy Stars in this series

No. 1	Snoopy Stars as The Flying Ace	£1.95
No. 2	Snoopy Stars as The Matchmaker	£1.95
No. 3	Snoopy Stars as The Terror of the Ice	£1.95
No. 4	Snoopy Stars as The Legal Beagle	£1.95
No. 5	Snoopy Stars as The Fearless Leader	£1.95
No. 6	Snoopy Stars as Man's Best Friend	£1.95
No. 7	Snoopy Stars as The Sportsman	£1.95
No. 8	Snoopy Stars as The Scourge of the Fairways	£1.95
No. 9	Snoopy Stars as The Branch Manager	£1.95
No. 11	Snoopy Stars as The Great Pretender	£1.95
No. 12	Snoopy Stars as The Dog-Dish Gourmet	£1.95

Colour landscapes

First Serve	£2.95
Be Prepared	£2.95
Stay Cool	£2.95
Shall We Dance?	£2.95
Let's Go	£2.95
Come Fly With Me	£2.95

Black and white landscapes

It's a Dog's Life	£2.50
Roundup	£2.50
Freewheelin'	£2.50
Joe Cool	£2.50
Chariots For Hire	£2.50
Dogs Don't Eat Dessert	£2.50
You're on the Wrong Foot Again, Charlie Brown	£2.50

Weekenders

No. 1 Weekender	£4.95

All these books are available at your local bookshop or news-
agent, or can be ordered direct from the publisher. Just tick
the titles you require and fill in the form below. Prices and
availability subject to change without notice.

Ravette Books Limited, 3 Glenside Estate, Star Road,
Partridge Green, Horsham, West Sussex RH13 8RA

Please send a cheque or postal order, and allow the
following for postage and packing. UK: 45p for one book
plus 30p for each additional book.

Name ....

Address ....

....